Houghton
Mifflin
Harcourt

INCLUDES
- School-Home Letter
- Vocabulary Game Directions
- Diagnostic Interview Assessment
- Daily Enrichment Activities
- Reteach Intervention for every lesson
- Chapter 2 Test
- Chapter 2 Performance Task
- Answer Keys and
  Individual Record Forms

ISBN 978-0-544-34267-5

14 15 16 17 18 0304 22 21 20 19 18

4500742514   B C D E F G

Contents

Dear Family,

My class started Chapter 2 this week. In this chapter, I will learn different ways to subtract. I will learn to write subtraction sentences.

Love, _____

Vocabulary

minus (−) part of a subtraction sentence that means "to take from"

$$6 \overset{minus}{-} 5 = 1$$

difference answer to a subtraction sentence

$$3 - 2 = ①$$

fewer smaller number of something 3 books and 2 bags, you have 1 fewer bag than books

Home Activity

Show your child two groups of household objects, such as spoons and forks. Have your child use subtraction to compare how many more or fewer. Use different amounts and different objects every day.

$$5 - 2 = ?$$

Literature

Look for these books in a library. Have your child compare groups of items using *more* and *fewer*.

More, Fewer, Less by Tana Hoban. Greenwillow Books, 1998.

Elevator Magic by Stuart J. Murphy. HarperCollins, 1997.

Carta
para la casa

Querida familia:

Mi clase comenzó el Capítulo 2 esta semana. En este capítulo, aprenderé distintas formas para restar. Aprenderé a escribir enunciados de resta.

Con cariño, _____

Vocabulario

menos (−) parte de un enunciado de resta que significa "quitar de"

$$\underset{menos}{6 - 5 = 1}$$

diferencia respuesta a un enunciado de resta

$$3 - 2 = ①$$

menos un número Cantidad menor de algo. Si tienes 3 libros y 2 carteras, tienes 1 cartera menos.

Actividad para la casa

Muestre a su hijo dos grupos de objetos que haya en la casa, como cucharas y tenedores. Pídale que use la resta para comparar cuántos objetos más o menos hay de cada tipo. Use distintas cantidades y objetos diferentes cada día.

$$5 - 2 = ?$$

Literatura

Busque estos libros en una biblioteca. Pídale a su hijo que compare grupos de cosas usando *más* y *menos*.

More, Fewer, Less por Tana Hoban. Greenwillow Books, 1998.

El ascensor maravilloso por Stuart J. Murphy. HarperCollins, 1997.

Going Places with GO MATH! words

Bingo

Word Box
add
compare
difference
fewer
minus (−)
more
subtract
subtraction
sentence

Materials
- 1 set of word cards
- 18 ●

How to Play
Play with a partner.

1. Mix the cards. Put the cards in a pile with the blank side up.
2. Take a card. Read the word.
3. Find the matching word on your Bingo board. Cover the word with a ●. Put the card at the bottom of the pile.
4. The other player takes a turn.
5. The first player to cover 3 spaces in a line wins. The line may go across or down.

Player 1

difference	more	compare
fewer	**BINGO**	subtract
subtraction sentence	add	minus (−)

Player 2

minus (−)	difference	subtraction sentence
add	**BINGO**	subtract
more	compare	fewer

© Houghton Mifflin Harcourt Publishing Company

Chapter 2   sixty eight **68A**

Child's Name _____ Date _____

Chapter 2 • Diagnostic Interview Assessment

Materials • two-color counters
       • connecting cubes

Skill/Item	Assess
Explore Numbers 1 to 4 Show random groups of 1, 2, 3, and 4 counters. Have the child point to the group that has 3 counters.	_____ identifies a group of 3
Numbers 1 to 10 Have the child use counters to show a group of 8 and a group of 5.	_____ identifies a group of 5 _____ identifies a group of 8
Use Pictures to Subtract Set out a row of 9 counters. Write 9 − 7 = _____. Have the child take counters away to show the subtraction and tell how many counters are left. Ask the child to connect 5 cubes. Write 5 − 2 = _____. Have the child show the subtraction using cubes and tell the difference.	_____ uses counters and connecting cubes to show subtraction _____ finds the differences

For intervention options, see TE p. 66.

Use Pictures to Show Taking From

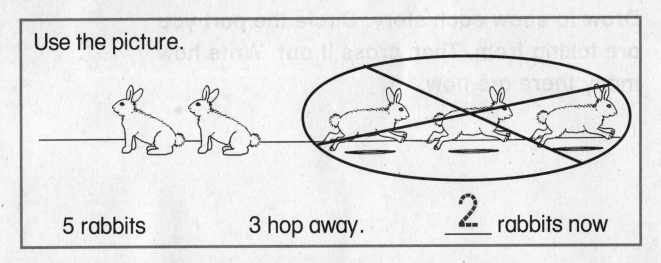

Use the picture.

5 rabbits   3 hop away.   __2__ rabbits now

Write how many there are now.

1.

8 birds   4 fly away.   _____ birds now

2.

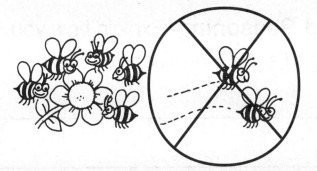

7 bees   2 fly away.   _____ bees now

Draw to Find the Difference

Draw to show each story. Circle the part you are taking from. Then cross it out. Write how many there are now.

1.

7 birds   5 birds fly away.   _____ birds now

2.

9 cows   6 cows walk away.   _____ cows now

 Writing and Reasoning Explain how you used your drawing to show Exercise 2.

_____

_____

_____

Model Taking From

Circle the part you take from the group.
Then cross it out.

3 dogs   2 dogs run away.   ___ dog now

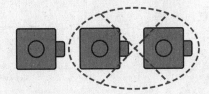

$3 - 2 = $ ___

Circle the part you take from the group.
Then cross it out. Write the difference.

1. 4 goats   2 goats walk away.   ___ goats now

$4 - 2 = $ ___

2. 6 ants   3 ants walk away.   ___ ants now

$6 - 3 = $ ___

How Many Are There Now?

**Solve. Complete the subtraction sentence.
Write the difference.**

1. Phong had 3 boxes.

He lost 1.

How many does he
have now?

_____ – _____ = _____

_____ boxes

---

2. There are 5 robins on a
branch. 4 robins fly away.
How many robins are
there now?

_____ – _____ = _____

_____ robin

---

3. Miss Smith had 8 stamps.

She lost 5.

How many does she
have now?

_____ – _____ = _____

_____ stamps

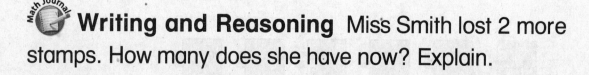 **Writing and Reasoning** Miss Smith lost 2 more
stamps. How many does she have now? Explain.

_____

_____

Model Taking Apart

You can use ◯ to **subtract**.

Sam has 6 cars. 4 cars are red.

The rest are yellow.

How many cars are yellow?

_2_ cars are yellow.

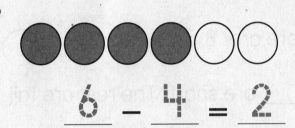

$$\underline{6} - \underline{4} = \underline{2}$$

Use ◯ to solve. Color. Write the number sentence and how many.

1. There are 5 books.
   I book is red. The
   rest are yellow. How
   many books are yellow?

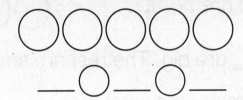

___ ◯ ___ ◯ ___

____ yellow books

2. There are 6 blocks.
   3 blocks are small.
   The rest are big.
   How many blocks
   are big?

___ ◯ ___ ◯ ___

____ big blocks

Find the Missing Parts

Write a number to complete the problem.
Color counters to show the problem.
Write a subtraction sentence to solve.
Write how many.

1. There are 8 🌼 .   ○ ○ ○ ○ ○ ○ ○ ○

   _____ are short. The rest are tall.

   How many are tall?

   _____ 🌼 are tall.   ___ ___ ○ ___ ○ ___

2. There are 9 🐰 .   ○ ○ ○ ○ ○ ○ ○ ○ ○

   _____ are big. The rest are small.

   How many are small?

   _____ 🐰 are small.   ___ ___ ○ ___ ○ ___

Writing and Reasoning Explain how to use ⬤ to check your answer for Exercise 2.

_____

_____

_____

Problem Solving •
Model Subtraction

There were 9 bugs on a rock. 7 bugs ran away.
How many bugs are on the rock now?

What do I need to find?	**What information do I need to use?**
how many __bugs__ on the rock now	_9_ bugs on a rock _7_ bugs ran away

Show how to solve the problem.

	7		2

9

$9 - 7 = \underline{2}$

Read the problem. Use the model to solve.
Complete the model and the number sentence.

1. There are 5 birds. I bird is
   big. The rest are small.
   How many birds are small?

	1		____

5

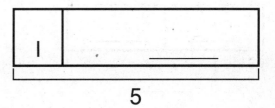

$5 - 1 = \underline{}$

What's For Lunch?

Read the problem.
Complete the model and the number sentence.
Solve.

1. Allie has 10 grapes. She eats
5 grapes. How many grapes
does she still have?

_____ grapes

_____ − _____ = _____

2. Mr. Dobbs makes 8 sandwiches.
He makes 1 peanut butter sandwich.
The rest are cheese. How many
cheese sandwiches does he make?

_____ cheese sandwiches

_____ − _____ = _____

Writing and Reasoning Write your own subtraction
problem. Use the bar model to solve your problem.

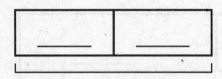

Use Pictures and Subtraction to Compare

You can subtract to compare groups.

$7 - 6 = \underline{1}$

There is 1 **more** than there are .

There is 1 **fewer** than there are .

Subtract to compare.

1.

$5 - 3 = \underline{}$

_____ more

2.

$6 - 4 = \underline{}$

_____ fewer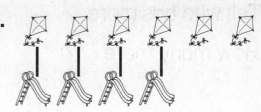

3.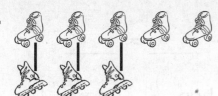

$4 - 1 = \underline{}$

_____ more

4.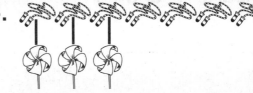

$7 - 3 = \underline{}$

_____ fewer

Solve the Story

**Draw a picture to compare. Complete the
subtraction sentence to solve.**

1. Geo has 6 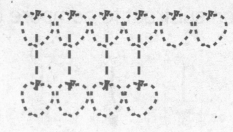.

   Lora has 2 fewer .

   How many does
   Lora have?

   ____ – ____ = ____

   _____ has ____ .

2. Dana has 8 .

   Gabe has 1 .

   Tell who has more .

   How many more ?

   ____ – ____ = ____

   _____ has ____ more .

Writing and Reasoning Geo and Lora have
10 . Dana and Gabe have 9 . Explain how to
compare and .

_____

_____

_____

Subtract to Compare

You can use 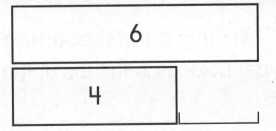 to show the bar model.

8 ● ● ● ● ● ● ● ●
6 ○ ○ ○ ○ ○ ○

Andy has 8 balloons.
Jill has 6 balloons.
How many more balloons
does Andy have than Jill?

| 8 |
| 6 | | 2 |

_____ more balloons

8 − 6 = 2

Read the problem. Use the bar model to solve. Write the number sentence. Then write how many.

1. Bo has 6 rocks.
   Jen has 4 rocks.
   How many more rocks
   does Bo have than Jen?

6 ● ● ● ● ● ●
4 ○ ○ ○ ○

| 6 |
| 4 | | ___ |

_____ more rocks

___ − ___ = ___

Get Ready for School

Write numbers for the problem. Use the bar model to solve. Write the number sentence.

1. Jay has _____ pencils. Jay has _____ more pencils than Ken. How many pencils does Ken have?

_____ ◯ _____ ◯ _____

2. Sam has _____ scarves. Sam has _____ more scarves than Jane. How many scarves does Jane have?

_____ ◯ _____ ◯ _____

3. Lee has _____ books. Lee has _____ more books than Amy. How many books does Amy have?

_____ ◯ _____ ◯ _____

Writing and Reasoning How do you know which number belongs in the top of the bar model in Exercise 3?

_____

_____

_____

Subtract All or Zero

When you subtract zero from a number, the difference is the number.

No ⬤ are crossed out.

$4 - 0 = \underline{4}$

When you subtract a number from itself, the difference is zero.

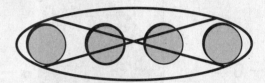

All ⬤ are crossed out.

$4 - 4 = \underline{0}$

Use ⬤. Write the difference.

1.

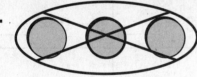

$3 - 3 = \underline{0}$

2.

$5 - 0 = \underline{}$

3.

$2 - 0 = \underline{}$

4.

$1 - 1 = \underline{}$

5.

$6 - 0 = \underline{}$

6.

$4 - 4 = \underline{}$

A Zero Picture

Write the difference for each box. Use a black crayon to color in each box that has a zero difference to find a picture.

$8 - 0 =$ ___		$6 - 6 =$ ___		$6 - 0 =$ ___
$1 - 0 =$ ___	$5 - 5 =$ ___	$7 - 0 =$ ___	$2 - 2 =$ ___	$4 - 0 =$ ___
$2 - 0 =$ ___	$1 - 1 =$ ___	$3 - 0 =$ ___	$3 - 3 =$ ___	$5 - 0 =$ ___
$6 - 0 =$ ___	$7 - 7 =$ ___	$2 - 0 =$ ___	$8 - 8 =$ ___	$8 - 0 =$ ___
$3 - 0 =$ ___		$4 - 4 =$ ___		$1 - 0 =$ ___

Writing and Reasoning Write the difference for the following problem: $0 - 0 =$ ____. If you are right, your answer will match the picture above.

Algebra • Take Apart Numbers

You can use ⬤ to take apart 6.

Circle the part you take away.
Then cross it out.

$6 - 5 = \underline{1}$

$6 - 4 = \underline{2}$

Use ⬤ to take apart 6. Circle the part you take away. Then cross it out. Complete the subtraction sentence.

1. ○○○○○○ $6 - 3 = \underline{}$

2. ○○○○○○ $6 - 2 = \underline{}$

3. ○○○○○○ $6 - 1 = \underline{}$

4. ○○○○○○ $6 - 0 = \underline{}$

Take Apart Seven

Write the missing numbers to complete the table to take apart 7.

1. ____	–	____	=	7
2. ____	–	1	=	____
3. 7	–	____	=	____
4. ____	–	3	=	____
5. 7	–	____	=	____
6. ____	–	5	=	____
7. 7	–	____	=	____
8. ____	–	____	=	0

 Writing and Reasoning What patterns do you see in the table?

_____

_____

Subtraction from 10 or Less

You can use  to help you subtract.

$$6$$
$$-3$$
$$\boxed{3}$$

$$3$$
$$-1$$
$$\boxed{2}$$

Write the subtraction problem.

1.

$$7$$
$$-4$$
$$\square$$

2.

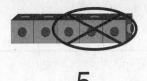

$$5$$
$$-3$$
$$\square$$

3.

$$8$$
$$-1$$
$$\square$$

4.

$$4$$
$$-2$$
$$\square$$

Complete That Sentence

**Draw and write to show
a subtraction problem.**

I.

2.

3.

Writing and Reasoning Draw your
own picture. Have a friend write the subtraction
problem that matches it.

1. Circle the part you are taking from the group.
Then cross it out. Write how many there are now.

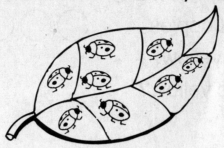

8 bugs   3 bugs walk away.   _____ bugs now

Circle the part you take away from the group.
Then cross it out. Write the difference.

2. There are 5 bees.
3 bees fly away.

5 − 3 = _____

3. There are 4 flies.
2 flies fly away.

4 − 2 = _____

---

4. Is the subtraction sentence true? Choose Yes or No.

6 − 0 = 0   ○ Yes   ○ No

3 − 3 = 0   ○ Yes   ○ No

1 − 0 = 1   ○ Yes   ○ No

5. Color  to solve. Write the
number sentence and how many.
There are 7 apples. 4 apples
are red. The rest are yellow.
How many apples are yellow?

○ ○ ○ ○ ○ ○ ○

_____ ◯ _____ ◯ _____   _____ yellow apples

---

6. Read the problem. Use the model
to solve. Complete the model and
the number sentence.

There are 8 cows in a barn. 2 cows are
brown. The others are white. How many
cows are white?

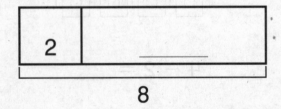

$8 - 2 =$ _____

---

7. Look at the picture. How many fewer plates
are there than cups? Choose the number.

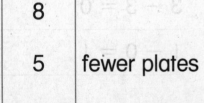

8

5   fewer plates

2

8. Read the problem. Use the
bar model to solve.

Blake has 5 caps. Callie has
2 caps. How many more caps
does Blake have than Callie?

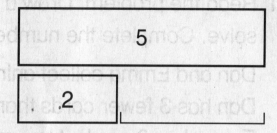

_____ caps

---

9. The models show two ways to take apart 4.
Complete the subtraction sentences.
Use these numbers.

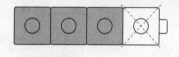

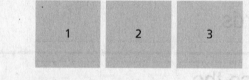

4 − ☐ = ☐

4 − ☐ = ☐

---

10. Write the subtraction sentence in the box
that shows the difference.

8   10   5
− 6   − 4   − 2

2	3	6
☐	☐	☐

GO ON ➡

11. Read the problem. Draw a model to solve. Complete the number sentence.

Dan and Emma collect animal cards. Dan has 3 fewer cards than Emma. Emma has 9 cards. How many cards does Dan have?

_____ – _____ = _____ cards

12. Write the subtraction sentence the picture shows.

Explain.

_____

_____

_____

Who's Still Here?

9 birds are in a tree.
Some of the birds fly away.
Now there are 6 birds in the tree.

1. Draw a picture to show 9 birds.
Cross out the ones that fly away.

2. Write a subtraction sentence about your picture.

9 − _____ = _____

3. The rest of the birds in your picture fly away one at a time. Complete the subtraction sentences to show how many birds are left each time.

_____ – _____ = _____

_____ – _____ = _____

_____ – _____ = _____

_____ – _____ = _____

_____ – _____ = _____

_____ – _____ = _____

4. What if all 9 birds fly away at the same time? Write a subtraction sentence to tell how many birds there are now.

_____ – _____ = _____

Subtraction Concepts

Who's Still Here?

COMMON CORE STANDARDS

1.OA.A.1 Use addition and subtraction within 20 to solve word problems involving situations of adding to, taking from, putting together, taking apart, and comparing, with unknowns in all positions, e.g., by using objects, drawings, and equations with a symbol for the unknown number to represent the problem.

PURPOSE

To assess the ability to represent and solve subtraction word problems within 10 using drawings and equations

TIME

25–30 minutes

GROUPING

Individuals

MATERIALS

- Performance Task, paper, pencil
- Two-color counters (optional)

PREPARATION HINTS

- Review using pictures to show "taking from" with children before assigning the task.
- Review writing subtraction sentences with children before assigning the task.
- Review vocabulary, including *subtraction sentence*.

IMPLEMENTATION NOTES

- Read the task aloud to children and make sure that all children have a clear understanding of the task.
- Children may use manipulatives to complete the task.
- Allow children as much paper as they need to complete the task.
- Allow as much time as children need to complete the task.
- Children must complete the task individually, without collaboration.
- Collect all work when the task is complete.

TASK SUMMARY

Children represent and solve subtraction word problems involving "taking from" a group by drawing pictures and writing equations.

REPRESENTATION

In this task, teachers can...

- Promote understanding by clarifying vocabulary using pictures.
- Provide options for comprehension by using cues to draw attention to critical features.

ACTION and EXPRESSION

In this task, teachers can...

- Provide options for physical action by offering counters to children while completing the task.

ENGAGEMENT

In this task, teachers can...

- Recruit interest by asking children to tell stories about their work.
- Provide options for self-assessment by offering strategies for checking work.

EXPECTED STUDENT OUTCOMES

- Complete the task within the time allowed
- Reflect engagement in a productive struggle
- Model and write equations to solve subtraction problems within 10

SCORING

Use the associated Rubric to evaluate each child's work.

Performance Task Rubric

WHO'S STILL HERE?

A level 3 response	• Indicates that the child has made sense of the task and persevered • Shows the ability to accurately model "taking away" from a group • Demonstrates understanding of what the parts of a subtraction sentence represent • Shows the ability to accurately apply concept of "taking away" to solve subtraction problems
A level 2 response	• Indicates that the child has made sense of the task and persevered • Accurately models "taking away" from a group • Demonstrates understanding of what the parts of a subtraction sentence represent • Shows the ability to accurately apply concept of "taking away" to solve subtraction problems • Addresses most or all aspects of the task, but there may be errors of omission
A level 1 response	• Shows that the child has made sense of at least some elements of the task • Shows evidence of understanding how "taking away" from a group can be modeled • Shows evidence of understanding of what the parts of a subtraction sentence represent • May not show the ability to accurately apply concept of "taking away" to solve subtraction problems
A level 0 response	• Shows little evidence that the child has made sense of the problems of the task • Reflects a lack of understanding of subtraction as "taking away" from a group • May not show the ability to accurately apply concept of "taking away" to solve subtraction problems • Shows little evidence of addressing the elements of the task

5. Color ● to solve. Write the number sentence and how many.
There are 7 apples. 4 apples are red. The rest are yellow.
How many apples are yellow?

Ⓡ Ⓡ Ⓡ Ⓨ Ⓨ Ⓨ

$7 - 4 = 3$

__3__ yellow apples

6. Read the problem. Use the model to solve. Complete the model and the number sentence.

There are 8 cows in a barn. 2 cows are brown. The others are white. How many cows are white?

8	
2	6

$8 - 2 = 6$

7. Look at the picture. How many fewer plates are there than cups? Choose the number.

8
5
(2)

___ fewer plates

1. Circle the part you are taking from the group. Then cross it out. Write how many there are now.

8 bugs   3 bugs walk away.   __5__ bugs now

Circle the part you take away from the group. Then cross it out. Write the difference.

2. There are 5 bees. 3 bees fly away.

$5 - 3 = 2$

3. There are 4 flies. 2 flies fly away.

$4 - 2 = 2$

4. Is the subtraction sentence true? Choose Yes or No.

$6 - 0 = 0$	○ Yes	● No
$3 - 3 = 0$	● Yes	○ No
$1 - 0 = 1$	● Yes	○ No

Name _____

11. Read the problem. Draw a model to solve. Complete the number sentence.

Dan and Emma collect animal cards. Dan has 3 fewer cards than Emma. Emma has 9 cards. How many cards does Dan have?

> Children may draw 2-color counters, connecting cubes, or a picture to show 9 items in all, 3 items crossed out, and 6 remaining items.

9 − 3 = 6 cards

12. Write the subtraction sentence the picture shows.

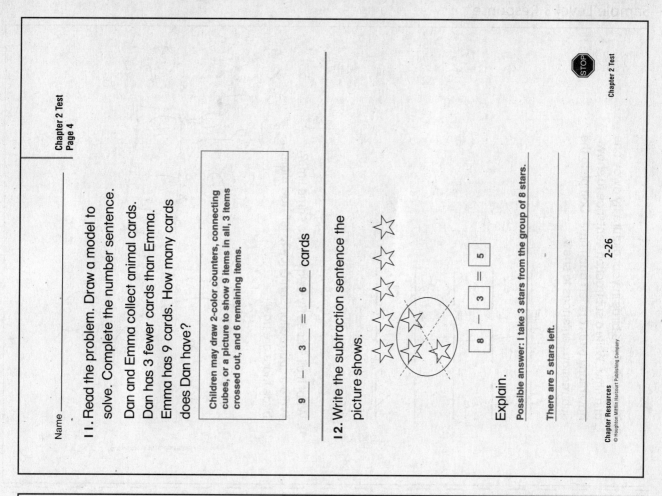

8 − 3 = 5

Explain.

Possible answer: I take 3 stars from the group of 8 stars.

There are 5 stars left.

Name _____

8. Read the problem. Use the bar model to solve.

Blake has 5 caps. Callie has 2 caps. How many more caps does Blake have than Callie?

5

2	

3 ___ caps

9. The models show two ways to take apart 4. Complete the subtraction sentences. Use these numbers.

1 2 3

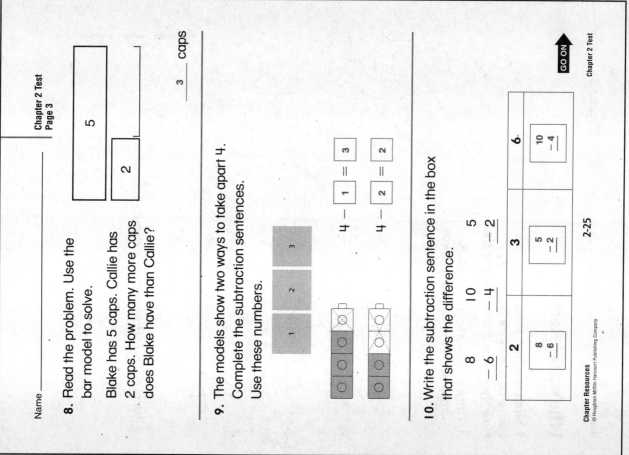

4 − 1 = 3

4 − 2 = 2

10. Write the subtraction sentence in the box that shows the difference.

8   10   5
−6   −4   −2

2	3	6
8	5	10
−6	−2	−4

3.

The rest of the birds in your picture fly away one at a time. Write a subtraction sentence to show how many birds are left each time. Complete the subtraction sentences to show.

$6 - 1 = 5$

$5 - 1 = 4$

$4 - 1 = 3$

$3 - 1 = 2$

$2 - 1 = 1$

4.

What if all 9 birds fly away at the same time? Write a subtraction sentence to tell how many birds there are now.

Chapter 2

Name _____

Who's Still Here?

9 birds are in a tree.
Some of the birds fly away.
Now there are 6 birds in the tree.

1. Draw a picture to show 9 birds.
   Cross out the ones that fly away.

2. Write a subtraction sentence about your picture.

$9 - 3 = 6$

Chapter 2

Name _____

Who's Still Here?

9 birds are in a tree.
Some of the birds fly away.
Now there are 6 birds in the tree.

1. Draw a picture to show 9 birds.
   Cross out the ones that fly away.

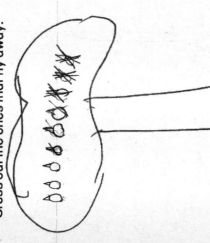

2. Write a subtraction sentence about your picture.

   9 − 3 = 6

© Houghton Mifflin Harcourt Publishing Company

---

3. The rest of the birds in your picture fly away one at a time. Write a subtraction sentence to show how many birds are left each time. Complete the subtraction sentences to show.

   6 − 1 = 4

   5 − 1 = 4

   4 − 1 = _____

   3 − 1 = 2

   2 − 1 = 1

4. What if all 9 birds fly away at the same time? Write a subtraction sentence to tell how many birds there are now.

   9 − 9 = 0

© Houghton Mifflin Harcourt Publishing Company

Chapter 2

© Houghton Mifflin Harcourt Publishing Company

Who's Still Here?

9 birds are in a tree.
Some of the birds fly away.
Now there are 6 birds in the tree.

1. Draw a picture to show 9 birds.
Cross out the ones that fly away.

2. Write a subtraction sentence about your picture.

$9 - 6 = 3$

3. The rest of the birds in your picture fly away one at a time. Write a subtraction sentence to show how many birds are left each time. Complete the subtraction sentences to show.

$6 - 1 = 5$

$5 - 1 = 4$

$4 - 1 = 3$

$3 - 1 = 2$

$2 - 1 = 1$

4. What if all 9 birds fly away at the same time? Write a subtraction sentence to tell how many birds there are now.

$9 - 0 = 0$

Chapter 2

Name _____

Who's Still Here?

9 birds are in a tree.
Some of the birds fly away.
Now there are 6 birds in the tree.

1. Draw a picture to show 9 birds. Cross out the ones that fly away.

2. Write a subtraction sentence about your picture.

$9 - 3 = 3$

3. The rest of the birds in your picture fly away one at a time. Write a subtraction sentence to show how many birds are left each time. Complete the subtraction sentences to show.

$3 - 1 = 2$

$2 - 1 = 0$

___ - ___ = ___

___ - ___ = ___

___ - ___ = ___

4. What if all 9 birds fly away at the same time? Write a subtraction sentence to tell how many birds there are now.

$9 - 0 = 9$

Chapter 2 Test

Item	Lesson	Standard	Content Focus	Intervene With	Personal Math Trainer
1	2.1	1.OA.A.1	Use pictures to show taking from.	R—2.1	1.OA.A.1
2, 3	2.2	1.OA.A.1	Model taking from.	R—2.2	1.OA.A.1
4	2.7	1.OA.D.8	Subtract all or zero.	R—2.7	1.OA.D.8
5	2.3	1.OA.A.1	Model taking apart.	R—2.3	1.OA.A.1
6	2.4	1.OA.A.1	Solve problems by making a model.	R—2.4	1.OA.A.1
7	2.5	1.OA.D.8	Use pictures to compare.	R—2.5	1.OA.D.8
8	2.6	1.OA.A.1	Subtract to compare.	R—2.6	1.OA.A.1
9	2.8	1.OA.A.1	Take apart numbers.	R—2.8	1.OA.A.1
10	2.9	1.OA.C.6	Subtract from 10 or less.	R—2.9	1.OA.C.6
11	2.4	1.OA.A.1	Model a subtraction word problem.	R—2.4	1.OA.A.1
12	2.9	1.OA.C.6	Use models and equations to identify solutions.	R—2.9	1.OA.C.6

Key: R—Reteach